itself is a pleasant central highland village lying in the heart of the Spey Valley and just 12 miles from Aviemore.

SPECIAL ATTRACTIONS One of the lowest annual rainfalls in Scotland. The Monadhliath Mountain range and the Cairngorm Plateau both on our doorstep offer a paradise Wilderness for the walker and birdwatcher. The Sportsman's choice includes golf, fishing, canoeing, sailing, windsurfing and pony-trekking. Ski-ing in the Cairngorms (usually Dec-May) 30 minutes away.

Dinner Bed and Breakfast £15.00-£19.00 per day incl. VAT.
Write or phone for Brochure and Leaflets.

AA • Relais Routiers • Michelin Guide • Good Hotel Guide

Self-catering luxury holidays are offered in this quiet, well-appointed, high-class park about 5 miles from Fort William on the romantic "Road to the Isles". The caravans are large modern units connected to mains services and are sited on broad landscaped terraces in a magnificent setting overlooking beautiful Loch Eil. There is a shop on site and facilities for boating and fishing.

EDINBURGH

Quite simply there's more to see and do in and around Edinburgh ... with its Castle, Palace, Festival, Tattoo, Zoo. Splendid museums and art galleries. Fine hotels, comfortable guest houses, restaurants and pubs. Unrivalled sports facilities.

Write today for free holiday folder and

---

welcome to Lochaber and the Scottish Highlands. From Fort William the whole lively canvas of the Highland panorama comes to life: sturdy villages nestling 'neath lofty peaks, the ruins of ancient castles — silent reminders of battles lost and won. The wild Rannoch Moor, eerie Pass of Glencoe. Yachts scudding across sunlit lochs. Skye, Oban, Inverness, Aviemore — all an easy day-drive away, with ample time to browse and absorb the local scene.

And Scotland's famous mountain, Ben Nevis, the beautiful ben, towering over Fort William, is there at the beginning, and end, of your tour, to welcome you or to "haste ye back"!

Save miles of motoring by visiting
DUMFRIES AND GALLOWAY

This beautiful corner of south west Scotland is a miniature of the Scottish countryside. It has mountains, moors, forests, lochs, rich green lowlands and a spectacular coastline. There is a network of really quiet back roads to explore where you will find charming villages, forest walks, ruined abbeys, old castles, museums, houses and gardens to visit. This region offers fishing, golf, sea angling, riding and pony trekking — all in a restful environment.

ON-SITE HOLIDAYS. Loch Lomond, Fort William, Oban and Dunoon areas. 4, 5, and 6 berth serviced and non-serviced caravans available. Prices from £30 per week.

SPECIALLY REDUCED ALL-INCLUSIVE TERMS — ALL SUMMER — AT A 1st CLASS SELECTION OF HOTEL AND CARAVAN ACCOMMODATION WITH EXCLUSIVE DISCOUNTS FOR PITLOCHRY'S WORLD FAMOUS NEW FESTIVAL THEATRE, SUMMER HIGHLAND NIGHTS VARIETY SHOWS AND LEGENDARY BLAIR CASTLE AND LOTS MORE.

See the 'Salmon Leap' at the Dam, visit a distillery, the Indoor Sports Centre, golf, fish for salmon, go boating, pony-trekking, hill and forest walking or just laze awhile amidst refreshing peace and beauty of hills, lochs, glens, and rivers — a tonic in any season.

Pitlochry is a 'Golden Rail' Resort.

Situated on the West Sutherland coast in the fishing village of Lochinver, this centrally heated 55 bedroom hotel (many of the bedrooms having private baths) offers cocktail and lounge bars, T.V. Lounge and excell...
a Table D'Hot...

"History is only a confused heap of facts."
- LORD CHESTERFIELD, *Letters to His Son.*

"All the historical books which contain no lies are extremely tedious."
- ANATOLE FRANCE.

"Anyone can make history. Only a great man can write it."
- OSCAR WILDE.

"Chiefs are pretty thick on the ground round Loch Earn. With a clan chowder of MacLarens, MacNabs, Stewarts, Macgregors...."
- JILLY COOPER, *The Scottish Chieftains.*
from SUPERJILLY.

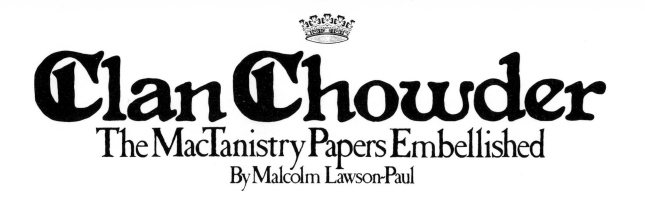

Clan Chowder

The MacTanistry Papers Embellished

By Malcolm Lawson-Paul

Debrett

For Kate of Clan Gunn
and Lucy Victoria.

Published by Debrett Peerage Ltd.,
73/77 Britannia Road,
London, S W 6

Designed and produced by
KEATS HOUSE LTD
10 Eastgate Square
Chichester, West Sussex PO19 1JH.

ISBN: 0 905649 56 7

Printed in Great Britain by The Pitman Press, Bath.

Introduction

The majority of people in these islands are familiar with the names, at least, of the major figures in Scotland's history. William Wallace and his war against the English, Bruce and the spider (or was he the one who burned the cakes?), Bonnie Prince Charlie, Flora MacDonald, and many others. But what of the lesser, yet as remarkable, characters who stood on the sidelines of events, or at most, fought only the minor skirmishes in the long brawl of Scotland's history?

Their songs would have remained unsung, and their stories untold, had it not been for a chance find at the Court of the Lord Lyon in Edinburgh in the summer of 1965. Whilst searching for old records and Sasines in the bicycle shed at New Register House, in order to give at least a patina of antiquity to a newly-created Life Peer, one of the young Pursuivants discovered a mildewed deed box. When opened up, it yielded the histories of several minor clans and personalities, hitherto forgotten, except to their chronicler, the prominent Scottish genealogist and antiquarian, Dr. Hamish MacTanistry, WS., FSA (Scot), Caithness Herald Extraordinary 1895-1907.

It is not generally known that those who fail to obtemper the Law of Arms in Scotland, or are found guilty of putting up 'false scutcheons' may be subjected to the thumbscrew until they recant. Her Majesty's Officers of Arms in Scotland, being kindly and humane gentlemen, seldom if ever, have recourse to such extreme measures, but in 1977 funds were required to pay for an extension to the Lord Lyon's Torture Chamber, including pantry and extended cellar space, as the Master of the Rack had complained that he and his assistants had "but little space wherein to refresh ourselves in our prolonged inactivity" as he quaintly put it.

Accordingly, it was decided to dispose of a number of miscellaneous MSS., and these were sold for ready money to passers-by at a hastily erected stall in the Lawnmarket, at which time they came into the author's possession, with permission to publish if desired.

To these have been added such warp of fact and weft of fantasy as seemed desirable, together with gleanings from selected journals, and eavesdroppings from such far-apart places as Puffins Club, the 19th Hole at Prestwick, and a chinese restaurant at Inverness.

It is, however, to be hoped that through the tangled weave of these pages will shine the author's genuine affection for his victims, together with a caveat to the reader that, as with the best porridge, the following histories should be taken with a large pinch of salt.

Malcolm Lawson-Paul.

Contents

The Biggin Folk
(3000 B.C. - 83 A.D.)

VENI · VICI
VIMPI

Almost five thousand years ago there was a vast influx of peoples from the plains of Northern and Central Europe to what later became known as Albainn, the land of the Scots. These included the Biggin Folk, whose ethnic origins are lost in the mists of antiquity, but certain it is that they had long been settled in what are now Annandale and Nithsdale before Julius Agricola came with his legions toward the end of the first century A.D.

From the artifacts they have left behind, such as gaming dice, scraps of food, jackets of donkey skin, and protective helmets, it is surmised that they were builders, confirmed rather than refuted, by an almost total absence of actual working tools. The helmets themselves are worthy of mention in that, having been first coated in a yellow pigment, they were then inscribed not with the name of the Emperor, as was the case with the common soldiery, but with the name of their own tribe, or 'insignae paternum', such as MacAlpini, Lagni, Uimpi, etc. There had been builders in Alba at earlier times, of course, inhabitants of small stone fortifications set in the middle of lakes, but the idea of swimming to work every morning never really caught on, and, after a few hundred years the design was quietly dropped.

There is early evidence that the invading legions used the indigenous tribes as a form of contract labour, in that, provided the builders promised to work all day, the military chargehands agreed not to kill them until the next shift clocked-on. Remains of some of their drinking vessels bear the crude Latin inscription;

IMPERATOR REX NERO. BONUM RESPONDIT UBIQUE.

— usually abbreviated in the Roman manner to the initials IRN.BRU., and is doubtless a form of loyal thanksgiving to the Emperor for contracts given. Julius himself instituted a libation bearing the name AGRI-COLA, but as this was found useful only for cleaning coinage, rather than human consumption, it was suppressed by Imperial Decree, and as a result he was recalled to Rome in 84 A.D. This is remarkable in that when the late Dr. MacTanistry (q.v.) was excavating the remains of the giant Iron Age football stadium at Callanish in the Outer Hebrides in 1900, several hundred tin drinking vessels were found bearing the name of the MacEwan tribe or clan, evidence of a more local loyalty the further from the seat of regional government. (Vide: 'The Forgotten League'. Reflections arising from the St. Andrews University Archaeological Society Expedition to the Western Isles, Summer 1900. MacTanistry Papers Folio IX. Published by The Scottish Record Society, 1946.). The Callanish stadium is also mentioned by Tacitus in his FASTI EDIFICII BRITANNICUM.

A Roman in the Gloamin'
(84 A.D. - 383 A.D.)

The twilight of Imperial occupation was heralded by the loss of the famous 9th Legion whilst crossing a bog, retreating after a skirmish with a local chieftain, Kilroy, whose name appears on many buildings and is still widely remembered. Their mascot, the equally famous Beagle of the Ninth, is said still to haunt the area, which is known to this day as Cu-Drumlie, or 'The Place of the Muddy Dog'.

In 121 A.D., tired of the interminable squabbles of his Pro-Consuls over the endings of irregular verbs, and greatly in need of a sabbatical, not to mention a bit of a fling on the side, the Emperor Hadrian himself visited Alba. He was accompanied by the great Coleburnus Magister, who, having already corrected the grammar in Julius Caesar's De Bello Gallico, was in search of fresh copy. Hadrian invited tenders from the Biggin tribes for the building of a great wall from the Solway to the Tyne. The Uimpi secured the contract by cutting their costs and using sub-standard stone imported from the area around

Caen, known as Gaulstones. Bonded together with nothing more substantial than river mud and chopped straw, the wall lasted a mere three months before being destroyed by the Winter weather.

Cutting his losses the Emperor returned to Rome and its verbal conflict, whilst Coleburnus departed south to Clausentum, where he founded a school for the teaching of Latin grammar to the Angles, the more tardy of whom were shipped to Rome for service at the Coliseum. The Roman historian Marcellus Mendax, writing at the time of the Emperor Constantine noted that many of the Imperial Lions soon turned-in their cards and opted for Vegetarianism and a free passage back to Africa rather than face these barbaric schoolboys.

Meanwhile, however, the wall had failed to repel the invading hordes from the north, and twenty years later the then Governor of Britannia, Lollius Urbicus, invited tenders for the building of another. The contract was this time secured by the Lagni, who demolished the Uimpi

wall with Pict and shovel in three weeks by working overtime, and transported it by dead of night in large vehicles or 'magna carta', re-erecting it on its new site. 'Scotorum inacessa Uimpi loca, Lagni vero subdita,' wrote Flagellus, the Roman Pro-Consul, who was present at the time, and who is there who could disagree with him?

Nonetheless, 'ere their perfidy could be discovered, the Lagni prudently withdrew south to Luguualium, or Carlisle, where they remained and prospered. By 383 A.D., disheartened by news from Rome and racked by chilblains, the Legions suffered their worst defeat at the battle of Antipasta, and withdrew to their sunny homeland and the eager pen of Mr. Gibbon. Alba had struck the first blow in the great struggle against the Treaty of Rome!

St Odorus
Monk and Hermit (542 A.D. - 612 A.D.)

When the great Christain missionary Columba arrived on the island of Iona in 563 A.D., among the small band of brothers accompanying him was a young novice whose original gaelic name we do not know, but who has come to be known to us as Odorus. Although friendly and gregarious by nature, and possessed of a humble piety, he was unfortunately somewhat less than particular in matters of personal hygiene, which, in a closed community, can pose serious problems. It was noted that during morning ablutions before the Office of Prime, he was loth to behold his reflection in a bowl of water, and would invariably donate his weekly ration of soap to his fellow monks. This was at first charitably accepted as an example of Christian unselfishness, coupled with a becoming lack of personal vanity, but after some little time it was noted that during the Asperges he would invariably flinch, and during the celebration of Mass at the words "Lavabo inter innocentes..." something akin to a violent seizure would overtake him, and he would collapse on the sanctuary floor, trembling uncontrollably, and hiding himself in the folds of his vestments. Demonic possession was at first suspected, but, exorcism having failed to produce the desired results, he was questioned by the Master of Novices. It transpired that during his baptism in his native Ireland, which at that period in the Celtic Church was by total immersion, he had slipped from the hands of a partly-inebriated cleric and almost drowned, resulting in his present total aversion to water.

His religious superiors having had no previous experience of this particular form of hydrophobia, he was at first sent to work in the monastery laundry as a form of therapy, but, his habits proving dirtier than those he was supposed to wash, he was soon transferred to the Piggery, where it was hoped that his charges would be less discriminating. This was violently disproved when the entire herd threw themselves over the cliff edge in a fair imitation of the Gadarene swine. Anonymous notes slipped under his cell door to the effect that 'cleanliness is next to godliness' had no effect, and the consumption of incense was rising to astronomical proportions.

Matters came to a head on Maundy Thursday 568 A.D., when, during the Mandatum Ceremony, the officiating priest refused point blank to wash Brother Odorus's feet in the customary manner. Early on Good Friday morning, under cover of darkness, his brother monks seized Odorus and bound him hand and foot. With muffled oars and faces they rowed him in a small boat north past the island of Coll, and after passing close to Ardnamurchan Point, deposited him on the small island of Muck, on Easter morning, there to live out his days as a hermit. As companion they co-opted the services of a moth-eaten mongrel of indeterminate ancestry and a faulty sense of smell, who was in need of human companionship. Odorus named him Fideo, which in its adulterated form of Fido, has been a popular name for dogs ever since.

In 590 A.D. the Viking raider Magnus Harebrain, on a raiding expedition to the Western Isles, was discouraged from landing by the sight of this dishevelled and malodorous apparition in a food-stained black monastic habit, and pursued his lunatic adventures elsewhere. Odorus was canonised by Pope Gregory XIII in 1576, in one of his lighter moments, and is the Patron Saint of soap makers. His Feast Day is 29th February.

Harald Harebrain
Viking Lord of the Orkneys (565 A.D. - 655 A.D.)

The last decade of the eighth century saw the full force of the great Norse incursions into these islands, which were to continue for the better part of two hundred years. In their langskips, or longships they came, — sleek hulls cutting through the grey northern waters, striped sails billowing in the stiff wind, serried ranks of brightly-coloured shields glistening in the wintry sun, their dragon figureheads hungry for prey.

Inspired by the stirring tales they had heard recounted in the great Norse Sagas, they were following the tradition set by the renowned explorer Harald Harebrain, who had sailed this selfsame way more than two hundred years earlier, eventually to become Lord of the Orkneys. In the same year that St. Columba was founding his monastery on the Isle of Iona, Harald Harebrain was born, fifth child of the great Viking Jarl Erik Snotbeard. Lacking the physical attributes of his four elder brothers, he was encouraged by his mother to pursue a career in furniture design, rather than the customary training in rape and pillage, which formed the educational norm at that time. However, resentful of their taunts, and egged-on by his drinking companion or skol-friend, Olaf the Unhinged, he secretly constructed a longship in his workshop. Being obliged to give his mother the impression, on her customary bedtime tours of inspection, that he was in fact assembling a dining table with matching set of thirty chairs, it was less than surprising that the project took several months to complete and assumed a somewhat bizarre appearance as time wore on. His workshop being situated on the third storey of his father's longhouse, transportation arrangements posed their own particular problems, and re-assembling at the launching site did little to improve the sea-worthiness of the strange craft.

His imagination fired by tales of travellers from Southern Europe, and avid for adventure, he eventually set sail from the Baltic port of Sunnoffagunn in 585 A.D. accompanied by some twenty-odd companions in arms,

was decided to settle in these pleasant islands and raise beef cattle, of which the blood line survives to this day, winning many prizes in highland cattle shows on the mainland.

The pyrotechnic experiments of Rank Aarsson had now reached such alarming proportions that Harald was obliged to banish him to the northern part of the island, where he soon succeeded in setting fire to his hut. As the hut was constructed of the local long thin slabs of stone, this was a feat in itself. In extinguishing the fire with sea water, a most pleasant sensation was remarked upon by his companion, Gunhilda Fairhair, and within a month she had established a flourishing Sauna business, where overtired warriors could relax. Bored with his new-found job as boilerman at the Sauna, Aarsson built himself a small boat and sailed northward to Shetland. Unfortunately, within sight of Lerwick he contrived to set fire to his boat whilst cooking a quick breakfast, and this spectacular act of self-immolation is still celebrated to this day. The Festival of Up-Helly-Aarsson, usually called Up-Helly-Aa, takes place every January, attracting many visitors.

The Orkneyinga Saga tells us that Harald Harebrain made one more voyage, this time to the Western Isles, and attempted a landing on the island of Muck in 590 A.D., but was so disconcerted by the sight of the dishevelled and black-habited Monk-Hermit Odorus walking on the beach, that he went smartly about and set sail for Orkney, vowing never to leave again. In 600 A.D., the local King of Orkney, known throughout the islands as the Old Man of Hoy, surrendered authority to Harald. "My kingdom for a Norse!" he giggled, as Harald was proclaimed Jarl of Orkney.

including the aforementioned Olaf, and one, Rank Aarsson, son of Vesta Swan-Neck, who was evading capture by the authorities after an incident involving a bonfire the night before. Proceeding on a westerly course through the Lagerfjord they ran into foul weather in Heligoland and, lacking seamanship ran aground on the Fair Isle. Their mainsail being lost, they were obliged to unravel their woollen tunics and fashion themselves another. The indigenous islanders, greatly impressed by the ingenuity of this multicoloured design, later adopted it in the now famous Fairisle pullover. Continuing south the intrepid adventurers successfully navigated the Westray Firth and eventually made landfall near the present site of Kirkwall. By common consent of the Thing, or Council, it

Scallywagge of that Ilk
(10th century et seq)

The surname 'Scallywagge' is probably originally derived from the Swedish 'Sköld Vagskura' or 'wavy shield', meaning one who changes sides, a turncoat.

Magnus *Skolvig* was Jarl of Caithness in the tenth century, siding with Ketil Flatnose when he rebelled against Harold Fair Hair.

Skolwigga was Bishop of Durham in attendance on Athelstan, according to the Anglo-Saxon Chronicle, when he met King Constantine II of the Scots at Bakewell, Derbyshire, in 961 A.D.

Kenneth *Skolwige* is mentioned in the Annals of Tigernach as Witness to the marriage of Bethoc, daughter of King Malcolm II to Crinan, Abbot of Dunkeld, but was not invited to the 'purvie' afterwards.

In 1174 Sir Gervase *Skulwagge* was present at the Treaty of Falaise between William the Lion and King Henry II of England, and his great-grandson Sir Cambric *Skulwage* appears as a signatory to the Ragman Roll of 1296, or at least would have, had he been able to write.

Janus *Skullwage* was found 'attired in the habite of ane woman' and hiding in a ditch at the Battle of Otterburn in 1388. His plea for clemency on the grounds of pregnancy was disallowed, and he was hanged at Jedburgh later the same year, near the present site of the Spread Eagle Hotel.

Jacques *de Sculwage* was Blanche Almond Pursuivant to the Duke of Burgundy in 1420, and his arms in the Armorial de l'Europe are blazoned;
"M. de Sculwage, party de argent et de vert, le visage d'un homme de l'n en l'autre."

The name *Scallwagge* is of great antiquity in Angus, and in 1590 Japhet Scallwagge, a soutar of Affleck, was accused with others of witchcraft at Dundee. Offering to turn King's Evidence, he was transformed into a hare by his co-defendants, and was roasted and eaten by the presiding judge that same evening, accompanied by red cabbage and apple, and washed down with an excellent bottle of claret.

Patrick *Skullwog* is listed on the Articles of Agreement of the Brigantine 'Blackbird' in 1714, where he is described as 'First Mate'. At one time suspected of engaging in the slave trade, he was made Deputy Governor of Jamaica in 1726.

William *Skilwoge*, a Corporal of Horse in Lord Aberdeen's Hussars was caught in a compromising position in the Crimean Campaign in 1855, with a Russian/English dictionary and 5,000 Roubles in his greatcoat pockets. Court-Martialled and imprisoned in the Tower of London, he was exchanged with Russia for 3,000 bottles of Stolichnaya Vodka, by Lord Palmerston in 1857.

Sir Jamie *Scallywagge* Bt., acted as Agent for the Khedive of Egypt in the Suez Canal transaction of 1875, and perished in the Tay Bridge Disaster four years later. In his Last Will and Testament he bequeathed 10,000 Ordinary Shares in the Suez Canal Company to his nephew, Hiram in Long Island.

Hiram B. *Scallywagg* III of Denver, Colorado, was Republican fund-raiser and Deputy Assistant Public Relations Officer to Richard Milhaus Nixon in his 1968 Presidential campaign. His present address is; c/o The State Penitentiary, Jackson, Mississippi, U.S.A.

Crispin Pillock
'Crispin Og'. False claimant to the Throne (c 1152)

It just wasn't fair, he thought, as he heaved yet another pile of pots over to the sink. "It jest isnae fair!" he corrected himself hastily, speaking aloud. Must try to keep up the old image. But what was the use? he asked himself, as he began to scour the grease from another cauldron. God! These Normans were filthy eaters! No point in reviving old glories. He was forgotten now. A mere footnote in the history books of future generations... 'Crispin Pillock, False Claimant to the Throne of Scotland, discuss in no more than three lines.' He laughed ruefully. *He* could have shown them! He could have done great things if they had only given him a chance. Fought great battles. . . made peace with the English, perhaps. . . no, that would have been *too* much. 'King Crispin I.'. . . he liked that. It had a nice ring to it. Who *was* Crispin, anyway? He racked his brain, trying to remember the old history lessons. . . Crispin?. . . Basket Maker?. . . no. . . a Weaver, perhaps. . . no — still not right. . . Shoemaker! Yes, that was it! St. Crispin the

Shoemaker. Not so very noble after all. Trust his father to name him after a shoemaker! No imagination, his father. Who would want to have a king named after some old cobbler. No dignity there. No style. Who would *ever* want to remember Crispin's Day? Still, it didn't matter now. Crispinian, perhaps, — now that sounded better. Sort of Latin feel. . .

He watched as a cockroach crawled painfully up the bare scullery wall, one step, two steps, three steps — and then a slither down to the ground again. Just like Life, he mused, — one moment you're on the up and up, azure skies for Crispin, and then suddenly — Bang! — it's all gone again — just like a soap bubble bursting. Which reminded him, and he bent to his duties, heaving another pot to the sink. The brown goo looked familiar, and he dipped his finger in. Yes — he had been right, — Venison stew it was. That brought back some memories all right. That had been after the Monastery at Holyrood. A lay monk at twelve, — not a bad life, the Monastery.

18

Prime, None, Matins, Vespers, Compline — same thing every day. A bit boring, perhaps, but safe at least. . . no one to beat you up every day, except for that silly flagellation bit every Ash Wednesday, and that Brother Devius with the wet lips and the nasty look in his eye as he wielded the discipline. Better than charcoal burning anyway, which was the only other career on offer at the time. Never fancied charcoal burning much. Too messy by half. Not as messy as this, though, he thought, and a little tear welled in his eye and plopped into the greasy water in front of him.

Just after Matins one morning it had happened. The old King, David I had just fallen off the perch the week before. Solemn speeches, candles, yards of black cloth, Requiem Masses, that sort of thing. And then, a couple of days later Father Abbot had sent for him, and the two important looking soldiers had stood there looking at him, like a bullock in the market.

"It's him to a tee," said the first one.

"Even got the mole on his nose!" replied the other.

"Dead ringer, if ever I saw one!" agreed the first.

"Same age too — give or take a month" said the first one.

"— Give or take a month," agreed the other.

"His own mother couldn't tell the difference," they both said. And then they had taken him away with them, and he remembered Father Abbot putting the leather bag into the folds of his habit. It had chinked. Like money.

Elocution lessons had followed, how to speak the Guid Scots Tongue. How to give orders. And table manners. How to hold your meat on the knife without spilling the gravy on your tunic. . . how not to swill your mouth out in your goblet. Important little things these — important for a king at least.

And the clothes! Red silk. . .blue satin. . .long cloaks trimmed with ermine and big collars. . .the lovely shining armour. And best of all the surcoat, with the Royal Arms of Scotland on it.

The Coronation had been fun too. Everybody crowding in to have a look at the new young King. Fanfares and lots of chanting. They had missed out the bit about his lineage. No time, perhaps. And it was a pity his parents couldn't be there. They would have been proud of him. He wondered briefly whether it hurt much having your tongue cut out. . . All the monks from his old Abbey were there, including Father Abbot, looking smug in his best vestments. He'd show them! — although the guards stood suspiciously close. Still, — better not to take chances. There were always too many loonies around. And then the old Bishop put the Crown of Scotland on his head, and everybody had cheered like mad.

Until that awful day when there had been a fight outside, and the new soldiers had come, and he had been taken in front of someone they all called 'The rightful King', and they had made him kneel. Events followed pretty quickly then.

"To the Scullery!" they said, "or it's off with your head!" "Take your choice," they said, so he had, and here he was, washing pots for life, without the option.

King Malcolm IV they called him — some called him the Maiden, Lord knows why, — there was nothing. . well, you know. . .poofy about him. Seemed quite a decent sort of bloke really, about the same age too. . . King Malcolm IV of Scotland, — yes, that would look good in the History books. Not as good as Crispin, though!

Black Donald MacAbre
'Donal Dubh'. Herbalist and Druggist (1517 - 1567)

Donald MacAbre was born in 1517, the unplanned issue of a fleeting and loveless union between one Meg MacAbre, and an itinerant tin-smith who was blind drunk at the time, and omitted to leave his name prior to his morning departure. From her small shop behind Edinburgh's Canongate Tolbooth, Mistress MacAbre was the proprietress and sole owner of the local Herbalist and Druggists, and from the recesses of her dark and dusty shop with its retorts and crucibles, jars of dried bats' wings, dragon's blood, and powdered rhinoceros horn, produced a variety of potions and preparations to cure everything from disorders of the bowels to unrequited love. It was therefore natural that upon his mother shuffling off her mortal coils and going to that great Crucible in the Sky, young Donald should inherit the family business, such as it was.

Although not possessed of formal education, he was a dab hand with the pestle and mortar, with a natural aptitude for business matters, and, despite his unprepossessing surname, a good line in sales patter. Once inadvertently omitting the essential ingredients from a mixture intended to remedy an overheating of the blood, he cannily observed that the effect upon his patient was just the same. Further experiments of a like nature confirmed his theory, and that mainstay of modern medicine, the Placebo, was invented. Ever-eager to capitalise on an expanding market, he experimented late into every night, and produced the prototypes of a large range of pharmaceutical and household products. Given the insanitary conditions prevailing in the back wynds of Edinburgh, he concocted a strong-smelling fluid for the cleaning of middens and outhouses. His original formula for this was lost for over four hundred years, but came to light in a London bookshop in the 1950's, since which time it has been adopted by at least one English brewery, who market it as their 'Best Bitter'.

It was in 1540 that he first fell in with one Thomas

Gray, a local chirurgeon, who was working on his now famous 'Anatomy in a Country Churchyard' — the standard handbook for Home Office pathologists, and who gave him the basis of a formula for a skin lotion he had discovered whilst researching Egyptian mummies, and based on olive oil and various middle eastern flower essences. Ever-mindful of changing fashions, and anxious to offer a new line to his growing band of regular customers, MacAbre brought out his own version, but was obliged to substitute fish oil and rose petals as ingredients in the recipe. The resultant noxious concoction was one of his few failures, and in trying to improve the formula one night, he only succeeded in over-heating it, setting fire to his own premises, and the ensuing conflagration rendered him homeless.

His regular drinking companion at this time was a man by the name of Nelson, servant to Henry Stewart, Lord Darnley, and the said Nelson's offer of temporary accommodation in the basement of his Royal master's house at nearby Kirk o'Field was gratefully accepted. It was here that his first experiments in the manufacture of a powder for whitening the teeth were conducted. Upon a small monetary consideration he was given use of the kitchen and cellars for his experiments, and by 1567 had perfected a tooth powder containing, among other ingredients, a modicum of gunpowder. One can only speculate upon events, suffice to say that his measurements were at fault, for at about 2 a.m. on 10th February 1567, the silent air around Kirk o'Field was rent with a mighty and violent explosion, reducing the house to a heap of rubble. As his presence in the house was not known, MacAbre was never suspected, and history has sought to place the blame for this unfortunate occurrence on James Hepburn, 4th Earl of Bothwell.

Robert Clootie
'Robert the Devil' (1560 - 1617)

That part of the Cairngorms north-east of Kingussie can be a bleak and desolate place in mid-Winter. When the cold December mists come down off Ben Macdhui and Braerich, filling Glen Ghoulie in a matter of minutes like an icy pool, woe to the traveller who does not know the route to Linn o' dee, for there are no roads here, and many have there been who, setting out with a light heart in fair weather, were soon engulfed in ghostly wraithes, never to be seen again. Little, if anything, has changed in the four hundred and more years or so since this was the haunt of one of the most notorious tobacco-hunters in the history of smoking. Robert Campbell of Glenlyon, a man of bloody reputation if ever there was one, was said to shudder at the very name of Clootie, and many years later, 'Butcher' Cumberland, marching north to Culloden and infamy, diverted his army several miles to the east, rather than pass the place.

Robert Clootie, an Attorney of mean disposition and similar aspect, entered the King's Service in 1580, having left Edinburgh University with a poor degree, and the reputation of a misfit. On account of friends at Court he was appointed Assistant to the Procurator Fiscal, in which position he proceeded to make life miserable for many, and thanks to a degree of fanaticism and a nit-picking attention to detail he found himself in good favour with his Sovereign. In 1590 he had shown a measure of favour in a case concerning an Heir of Entail, brought by one, Euphemia Chanty, known as the Fair Maid of Perth, after whom he had lusted. She had, however, spurned his advances, and his discomfiture was exacerbated when he later learned from a shipmaster at Leith, that she had emigrated to the New World, where she was now the contented wife of a prosperous tobacco farmer, and revered by the local Indian tribe, who had nicknamed her 'Passing Cloud' on account of her lightness of foot.

His Majesty King James VI, the well-known author and Royal fun-person, had published his 'Demonology' in 1597, and, with his strong aversion to smoking, had followed this up with another best-seller — 'A Counterblast to Tobacco' in 1604. With the Discovery of the Gunpowder Plot in 1605, he developed a strong dislike of naked lights of any sort, and is reputed to have eaten his food cold for the remainder of his life.

In 1606 the Statute 'de Fumificare' came into force, which proscribed the smoking of tobacco in any form, on pain of execution. Officers for the hunting and apprehension of smokers were appointed and despatched to the main centres of the Kingdom. This was the chance Robert Clootie had been waiting for, as he could see the opportunity both to advance his nefarious career, and at the same time strike an indirect blow at la Belle Chanty. With a measure of influence and the provision of a young man for his Royal Master's pleasure, he gained an appointment at Kingussie, where he fell to his task with a will. His Modus Operandi was contained in the 'Discours des Sorciers' by Henri Boguet, which had been published in 1590. Notices were posted in Kingussie that the smoking of tobacco was injurious to health, insofar as those caught doing so were liable to fine and imprisonment, whilst obdurate cases were consigned to the stake. The import of tobacco was prohibited, and the manufacture of clay tobacco pipes was punishable by five days in the stocks, and confiscation of all wares. All premises were liable to search, and suspected smokers could be put to the question. The tell-tale marks of nicotine stains were looked for on fingers. Old Nicotine, or Old Nick the Tobacco Imp, was decried from Market Cross and pulpit alike, and a spent match or tinder box spelt death to the offender.

In July 1610 Clootie obtained information from one William Ashe, a reformed smoker of cowardly mien,

known as the 'Craven A' that a coven of tobacco smokers was due to meet in a wood on the slopes of Ben Macdhui. Clootie and three officers hurried to the spot, and soon smelt the unmistakable aroma of best Straight Cut. Several arrests were made that night, including Ogden Player, soutar of Inverness, who was sentenced to have his pipes cut, Lambert Butler, hatter, also of Inverness, Virginia Woodbine, the blonde wife of the Baillie at Kingussie, known as Golden Virginia, William Wiffe, travelling knife-grinder, of no fixed abode, and Benson Hedges, mole-catcher of Aviemore, who later turned King's Evidence. On 15th August 1610 they were sentenced to be burned, slowly and evenly at Inverness near the site of Queen Mary's House in Bridge Street. Robert Clootie survived until 1617, but it is chronicled that toward the end of his life he had a nasty cough.

Dr James 'Orlop' MacMidden
Ships Surgeon (1614 - 1698)

A perusal of the Minutes of the Royal College of Surgeons of Edinburgh might reveal the name of James 'Orlop' MacMidden, whose name briefly became a byword for experimental surgery and novel medical techniques among seafarers of the seventeenth century. Born in Edinburgh in 1614, MacMidden was the son of a barber with premises near the Canongate. His interest in surgery developed from an early age, and a technique for the speedy removal of skelfs from the knee by the utilisation of an unsterilised skean dhub, is chronicled in the Memoirs of his erstwhile schoolfriend, Major-General Sandy 'Peg-Leg' Farquharson.

Apprenticed to his father at the age of fourteen, his surgical ambitions soon became rumoured in the vicinity, and it was hardly surprising that his father's more timorous customers, disconcerted by the speculative gleam in his youthful eye, became increasingly reluctant to be shaved by him. The administration of a physic to a local cat did not endear him to the neighbourhood, and

was the cause of the facial scratches which marked him for the remainder of his life; an unauthorised, less-than-successful attempt at open-heart surgery on the Minister's horse was the deciding factor in his father, mindful of the necessity to protect his own livelihood, to enter him at the University in order to qualify. During his period at the University he became a familiar figure to the citizens of the capital, although it must be stated that his habitual loitering around the Court of Session, striking bargains for the corpses of executed criminals in order to further his anatomical experiments, did little to enhance the reputations of either the Law or Medicine. It was at this time that he first entered into correspondence with the celebrated Bavarian physician Johann Rudolph Glauber (1603 - 1668), the MSS of which is preserved at the University of Heidelburg.

Gaining his Licentiate, he practised in Edinburgh with a modicum of success, until the visit of King Charles to the capital in 1633, whereupon he attached himself to the

Royal retinue as Assistant-Surgeon-in-Ordinary, and proceeded to London. Once in London he came under the influence of his contemporary, the great Thomas Wharton, and claimed to be instrumental in the discovery of Wharton's Duct of the submandibular salivary gland, which he constantly referred to as 'MacMidden's Duct.' During the interregnum, having no taste for Puritanism, and fearful of sharing the fate of his Royal master, he went to sea, finding himself a berth as Surgeon's Mate, aboard the privateer brig 'Blackadder'. He applied himself diligently to his duties, and in the heat of an engagement would be found on the Orlop deck, where he plied his ghastly trade, oblivious to smoke and gunfire, immersed in the task of patching-up his shipmates from the spare parts around him. He was present at the action off Tangier in 1655, when his vessel was caught off a lee shore by the notorious Barbary pirate Abdul Agogo, and only escaped by the skilful seamanship of her Captain, Jacob Skullwog, grandfather of Patrick Skullwog (q.v.)

During this engagement, one of Skullwog's legs was shattered by grapeshot, and MacMidden performed an amputation, working in the most trying conditions. That the wrong leg was amputated in the heat of battle, was due as much to the intoxication of the Chief Surgeon,

William Waucht, as to any incompetence on MacMidden's part. In the event, a tolerable pair of replacement legs was improvised from the remains of a broken forestay. MacMidden's Retractor, now standard surgical equipment, was also invented at this time, by adapting a pair of nutcrackers. Sharing a considerable amount of the prize money resulting from the capture of the Spanish galleon 'Santa Lucia de Paella', enabled him to come ashore in 1672, settling in Dumfries, where he purchased a comfortable if not commodious house in Bank Street.

It was whilst living here that he embarked on his protracted courtship of Priscylla Charybdis, daughter of a Huguenot ferryman at Rockcliffe. That their liaison came to naught was by reason of her father's reluctance to lose the services of a strong oarswoman, but the passage of their courtship is movingly recorded in a ballad, 'Aye o'er the Ferry' by Robert Burns, a later resident of the town. The receipt of his M.D., from the University of Edinburgh in 1675, was followed by many years of painstaking research, which became the foundation of the work of the Hunter brothers in the following century. In 1697 he was introduced to William Paterson of Dumfries, who persuaded him to invest a large amount of his capital in a company to found a colony on the coast of Darien on the Isthmus of Panama, and MacMidden himself sailed as Chief Surgeon with the expedition when it sailed from Leith in July 1698. The venture was however, doomed to failure, and he perished later the same year, succumbing to swamp fever. A case of his instruments was for many years on display at the entrance to the Faculty of Medicine at the University of Edinburgh, but was stolen in the 1950's.

Alasdair MacNimbus of Kelpie
South Sea Settler (1640 - 1744)

Alasdair MacNimbus of Kelpie was born in 1640 on the tiny island which bears his illustrious name, at the south-western tip of the Outer Hebrides. The island of Kelpie itself received a favourable mention by Dr. Samuel Johnson when he visited it in the company of James Boswell in 1773, on account of the bountiful hospitality he received at the hands of its inhabitants after having fallen into a burn, "... up to my neckclothe, which was exceeding soiled." The good doctor was revived with copious draughts of the local Uisge Beatha, — the fact that this was the cause of his original mishap being tactfully forgotten.

The younger son of Ruaridh Mor MacNimbus, the Poet Laird, the young Alasdair enjoyed a carefree childhood on his island home, but, unable to curb the naturally adventurous spirit of youth, and fearing the resultant impending paternity suit, he obtained his father's blessing and took ship from Oban in 1661 to seek his fortune in the South Seas. After numerous adventures, including a sea-battle with the notorious Dutch privateer Pieter van Djokstraap, 'The Frying Dutchman', he was caught in a violent storm somewhere in the region of latitude 20° south, and cast ashore upon a tropical island, the sole survivor of that unhappy voyage.

Lacking the means whereby to effect his escape, and mercifully spared the questionable blessings of gramophone records and encyclopaedias, his natural Hebridean instincts re-asserted themselves and he soon reconciled himself to his fate. The indigenous plant life provided both cotton and vegetable dyes of surpassing beauty, and, with the aid of a sett stick his mother had given him prior to his departure, he eventually produced tartan cloth which, traded with neighbouring islanders as a novel change from the more customary grass skirt, brought a modicum of affluence to the island, to the gratitude of its native population. Having learnt of the Hanoverian succession from his exchanges with passing vessels, he many times refused their offers of repatriation, and died, a happy and contented man, at the age of 104. The area, now known as the New Hebrides, is the only Gaelic-speaking community to be found in Polynesia.

Sir Archibald Cheetie
Secret Agent and Mole Breeder (1665 - 1709)

Archibald Cheetie, only son of William Cheetie the Arctic explorer, was born at Drumkellog Farm, near Peebles, in 1665. His father having perished for lack of sufficient woollen underclothing in the expedition of 1670, he was brought up by a doting mother, and given free run to express his childish tantrums. The local dominie, refusing him admittance to school by reason of his foul language and bullying manner, he was given the benefit of a tutor at home. This last, one Duncan Baggewashe, Doctor of Divinity of the University of Geneva, stood for little nonsense, and was handy with the tawse. A precocious talent for learning, particularly in the Natural Sciences, brought him an early place at Cromwell College, Cambridge, where he specialised in the study of Biology and developed a taste for claret and a neat line in political invective. A brilliant and industrious scholar, he gained a First in the Natural Science Tripos, but nevertheless was unpopular with his tutors on account of his secretive habits and taciturn manner. With the benefit of hindsight

it is possible to conjecture that it was here that he was first approached by an agent of the King of France, and recruited into that country's Intelligence Service. He specialised in the study of Moles, particularly the species *Talpa Europaea,* and obtained the post of Keeper of the King's Verdure, which was an ideal cover for his secondary activities. Of hirsute and unsavoury appearance he was once mistaken for a common vagrant and locked in the Fleet prison for two nights before an Officer of the Royal Household had, albeit reluctantly, to vouch for him.

His total ignorance of any language other than his own was almost his undoing, as, in order to understand the written instructions sent to him from Paris, he was obliged to make a standing arrangement with a French innkeeper at Rotherhythe, in exchange for a regular supply of moles, which marinated in red wine, were considered a great delicacy in certain quarters. By way of a 'dead letter box' he cunningly utilised an empty despatch box under a bench in the House of Commons, as he correctly surmised that this was the last place one might chance upon documents of a sensitive nature.

During the 1680's he published a successful paper on the life-cycle of the fur mite *Labidophorus Soricis*, and, under instructions from his masters in France, commenced his underground activities in the Park at Hampton Court, with the introduction of several families of moles. History records that whilst riding here on 20th February 1702, King William broke his collar bone, having fallen from his favourite mount, Sorrel, which had stumbled over a mole hill, finally succumbing to his injuries on 8th March.

Although questions about Cheetie's activities were asked, and he was named in Parliament, his friends at Court protected him, and he found himself free to leave England within a few days. Even when the despatch box was produced from under a Commons bench, it was dismissed as a Minister's luncheon box, and the matter was dropped. When an aggrieved French innkeeper arrived at the Houses of Parliament, enquiring about his regular supply of moleflesh, and willing to tell all, the only Minister with a sufficient knowledge of French was away for the weekend, and he was sent packing with half a guinea for his troubles. Upon arrival in France, Cheetie was awarded a state pension, and made an Officer of the Order of Anjou.

He lived out the remainder of his days in a small state apartment on the outskirts of Paris, anxiously enquiring of news of his old college and the latest racing results from Newmarket. At times of an evening he would become lachrymose, and stumble from room to room shouting a toast to the 'little gentleman in black velvet'. It was during such a bout that he fell from an upstairs window one evening in 1709, breaking his collar bone, from which injuries he died some days later. The French Government, having no further use for him, afforded him only a pauper's funeral, and he was buried in a common grave near the present site of the Gare de l'Est.

Lady Agnes Niblick
Golfer, inventor of the Tartan shopping trolley (1710 - 1760)

The ancient Norse tribes aspired to Valhalla, and modern man may dream of any one of several versions of Heaven, but to the true and dedicated golfer, the Royal and Ancient Course at St. Andrews represents earthly Paradise. Imagine the sun of a late Spring morning as it streams across the links of the Old Course, sharply contrasting the greens against the hazy blue sky, warming the Clubhouse roof. A stiff breeze from the sea teases the little flags marking each successive hole, like the pennons of a crusading army in battle array. Blackbirds chatter unseen from the nearby hedgerows, and, far overhead, a skylark sings his hymn of praise, interrupted only by the *thwack* of club hitting ball. Little knots of golfers in twos and fours, each with their attendant caddies, slowly meander across the links. Those players inadvertently getting themselves buried in the bunker adjacent to the notorious 11th or "Sea" hole, might find, peeping through the sand, a small stone plaque inscribed with the legend 'A.N. 1760'. Should their curiosity be whetted by

this small memorial, they might ask the Secretary to show them the Archives of the Royal and Ancient, wherein is set down the story of Lady Agnes Niblick. Agnes was born Agnes Goulash, elder daughter of Dr. Robert Goulash, founder and first headmaster of Goulash Academy, Glasgow, which was at one time the recognised preparatory school for Barlinnie, until forcibly closed down by the Butler Education Act of 1944.

In 1735, finally realising the futility of attempting to instil even a modicum of grammar and civilised behaviour into her father's unruly pupils, and unwilling to sacrifice her best years to being regularly nailed-up in the broom cupboard every Friday night, she quit Glasgow and settled for the tranquility of St. Andrews, where she took work as a domestic servant to the Bursar at St. Salvator's.

Whilst taking an evening walk on the seashore near the cathedral ruins, she caught the eye of the sporting 5th Earl of Niblick, who was practising his swing, and who soon afterwards gained her hand in marriage as she

struggled with his bag of clubs at the 14th hole. There followed ten years of blissful servitude, until the Jacobite Rising of 1745, whereupon Lord Niblick lost his heart to Prince Charles Edward Stuart, and his head on Tower Green to King George II.

Upon the formation of the Royal and Ancient Golf Club in 1754, Lady Agnes Niblick was given honorary Life Membership, and was instrumental in the invention of a club with a strongly sloping head and useful for bunker shots, which still bears her illustrious name. Although a popular clubhouse member, with a prodigious capacity for ginever and an amusing fund of stories, she was on account of her gender, prohibited the services of a caddy, whereupon her inventive mind gave birth to a small, wheeled trolley in which to carry her own clubs, and which is probably the forerunner of that scourge of the supermarket, the tartan shopping trolley.

She was accidentally struck by an errant golf ball in her fiftieth year, whilst standing at the 11th Hole, and as a singular mark of respect by the R and A. Committee, was interred on the selfsame spot.

The Sobieski Gang and others
Tartan Smugglers (fl 1746 - 1782)

BHUALLDH MI LE BATA

Following the Culloden fiasco a brutal Whig Government, determined to destroy the clan system, passed the infamous Dress Act of 1746, prohibiting the wearing by men or boys of tartan, kilt, or plaid, on pain of transportation. Women and soldiers were exempted from the Act, and clansmen were reduced to the unenviable choice of taking the King's Shilling or posing as their own sisters — thus inviting the unwelcome attentions of the selfsame soldiery. Hitherto the rag trade had been strictly a clan affair, but with Prohibition the rap was now too heavy, and the big operators moved in.

The Sobieski Brothers, immigrant Poles claiming kinship and a Royal Warrant from the Old Pretender's wife, opened a kilt hire and garment business over a baker's shop in Nairn, and patented the Quick-Release sporran, a valuable time-saver in emergencies. With their mail-order catalogue, called 'Vestiarium Scoticum', a full-colour 'Find YOUR Tartan' chart, and same-week delivery by mail coach under plain brown wrapper, they quickly cornered the retail market in the Grampian Region, opening a fish-oil business in Aberdeen where the money could be 'laundered'. The Wilson Boys, operating from an Edinburgh basement, opened-up the Lowland market with a nifty line in cheap continental tartans smuggled in through Leith, and diversified the racket to running 'Luckenbooths' or locked booths in the Royal Mile, where tartan could be indulged in, away from prying eyes.

Meanwhile, however, the Government was not inactive; specially-trained border collies were brought in to sniff-out illicit looms, which were confiscated and burnt on sight. And few there were who could not tell of a midnight knock on the door, and a brother or son, caught in possession of an illegal sporran, who was marched away, never to be seen again. 'Kilt Row' in Barlinnie Jail was full to overflowing; shoot-outs with government agents were frequent, and bodies, their sporrans weighted with lead shot, were found in secluded sea lochs. Small-town freebooters such as 'Legs' Cairn-Gormless — 'the shortest kilt in the West', and the Pillock Brothers from Govan, with their steel-toed ghillie shoes, were joining the action, the price war was hotting-up, and the export market beckoned. Already tartans with names such as Morgenstern, Abdullah, Dress Ferrari, and Hunting Kawasaki were on the drawing board, and the future looked bright.

In November 1760 the 'capos' from each firm met over the 'Prince Charlie' take-away haggis and neep shop in Kirkintilloch, and divided-up the territories. The Sobieski Gang kept the north and west, the Wilson Boys taking the Lowlands, and all having a slice of the Luckenbooth racket. Two days later, however, some of the Sobieski

Gang, led by Angus 'Neeps' Mac Sporran, caught the Wilson Boys, led by the notorious 'Baby Face' MacHismo, red-handed, pilfering their stock from a Leith warehouse. The resultant musket battle, known later as the St. Andrew's Day Massacre, claimed fourteen lives, and gave Wilson's a monopoly market. This they held for the next hundred years, obtaining Government contracts for supplying the newly-raised Gordon Highlanders in 1793, and Queen Victoria's favourite Dagenham Girl Pipers in 1860.

In 1782 Prohibition was repealed, but the country was slow to return to its old ways, and it was left to men of vision such as Ranald MacAroni of MacAroni and Sir Walter Scott to re-kindle Scotland's pride in the 'Garb of Old Gaul'.

Did You Know?
A Miscellany of Misinformation

1 The Forth Rail Bridge, built in 1890, was originally designed for Wellington Harbour, New Zealand.

2 In 1818 fragments of a dinosaur's jawbone were excavated from the foundations of Dunfermline Abbey.

3 After three years' service at the Bar, a Scottish advocate may exchange his horsehair wig for one of silk.

4 There are no cats on Mull.

5 In the Argyll and Sutherland Highlanders, Haggis is always eaten whilst standing.

6 By an unrepealed law of King Malcolm IV, the Lord Provost of Edinburgh still holds Droit de Seigneur over brides married on Midsummer's Day.

7 Potatoes were first introduced to Scotland in the reign of King James III, when they were used, not for the table, but for starching linen.

8 German forces landed on Staffa in 1942, but were repulsed by the islanders.

9 Until 1924 it was illegal to kill a spider in the Royal Burgh of Stirling.

10 Glasgow Rangers Football Club was founded with a bequest from the will of Archbishop Beaton.

16 Black Bun is distributed free to pensioners in Tannochbrae on Easter Saturday.

17 At The University of St. Andrews, Bejants, or first-year undergraduates, must wear yellow garters on Sundays.

18 The mother of Pontius Pilate was a Scotswoman of Clan Menzies.

19 In the fourteenth century, a Royal Licence was required to keep rabbits, in order to protect the market for beef cattle.

20 The main shopping precinct at Cumbernauld, Dumbartonshire, is haunted by the ghost of a Roman centurion.

11 In Moffat churchyard there is a tombstone recording the burial in 1637 of a woman who had given birth to a lamb in 1635.

12 The Archbishop of St. Andrews and Edinburgh has right of disposal over any whale cast ashore on the Fife coast.

13 There are more Americans in Aberdeen than there are in Long Island.

14 During Lent Term, Scottish Judges wear a hair shirt next to the skin.

15 The Stone of Destiny in Westminster Abbey is a replica of the original, rehabilitated in 1950.

Deacon Brawlie
Cleric and Fight Promoter (1755 - 1810)

Few stories in the troubled history of the Kirk are as strange as that of William Brawlie, MA., Deacon of Tron Kirk, 1795-1800. William Arbuthnot Brawlie, second son of a Quartermaster-Sergeant serving with Lord Linament's Horse, was born in the married quarters of the Edinburgh Garrison in 1755. Originally destined for the Army, but being somewhat consumptive in body and choleric by nature, he was considered by his schoolmasters at George Heriot's to be more suited to Holy Orders. Graduating from the University of Edinburgh he was ordained in 1776. Little is heard of him until an entry in the Records of the Court of Petty Session for March 1797"… for fighting for the possession of ane cambric shirt with ane Martha Gunn, washerwoman, and the Common Pump in the Lawnmarket, and for breaking ye King's Peace, Wm. Brawlie, Deacon, fined V schillings and bound over to bee of goode behaviour herefrom."

On the following Sunday in Tron Kirk, heavily bandaged, supported on crutches, and aching in every limb, he preached a sermon on the text:

> *"And Rachel said, 'With great wrestlings have I wrestled with my sister, and I have prevailed."*
> *(Genesis Chapter Thirty, verse eight)*

His confrontation with Gunn, and his choice of text, inspired the notion of promoting wrestling matches between members of the fair sex, and the idea once born, was eagerly received by a congregation long bored out of its collective mind by closed hostelries and a dearth of Sabbath entertainment. Under the aegis of his Mission for the Redemption of Fallen Women, Brawlie recruited his combatants, promising them a share of the 'gate money' collected during Morning Service. On Sunday evenings, after curfew, scurrying figures, lighted by link-boys, would enter the candle-lit gloom of the Crypt, there to join a sea of excited, sweating faces. Elders doubled as ushers, hot meat pies were on sale, snuff boxes passed hands, wagers were made, and small fortunes were won and lost on such favourites as 'Filthy-Breeks Bessie', 'The Canongate Crusher', and others. The foreshore of the Forth was scoured and 'Women Wrestling in Mudde' soon gained popularity. Disaster struck when one of his erstwhile protegees, one Jeanette Bizzem, better known to her fans as 'Jeanie the Jawbreaker', felt herself cheated by Brawlie of her purse from her celebrated bout with 'Morningside Maggie — The Dirtiest Fighter in Midlothian', which the said Bizzem had won in the third round with two throws and a pinfall. The case was laid before the Authorities. The Crypt, now better known as 'Brawlie's Kirk Circus', was raided, and a colourful era was at an end.

Public morality was outraged, and of little avail was the case for the Defence, that the accused was an ill-used cleric, intent only on keeping young women off the streets at night and of securing future Olympic hopes. The Judge, Lord Justice Hector Lammastide, had recently lost a goodly sum with an ill-advised wager on 'Greyfriars Gertie the Grassmarket Gouger', and his wife was beginning to ask awkward questions. "We wrestle not with flesh and blood — Ephesians Chapter Six, verse Twelve," shouted the defendant, as he was sentenced to seven years' transportation. "Thou art a stranger and an exile — Second Samuel, Chapter Fifteen, verse Nineteen!" riposted the Judge with a chuckle, adding that it was 6-4 odds against his ever returning to the City; an over-eager Juryman who shouted: "10-1 the favourite!" was put in the stocks for the rest of the day.

By way of an Epitaph, the Brawlie Belt is still fought for in Antipodean women's wrestling circles, and was recently won by 'Mauling Molly the Melbourne Masher'.

MacIcarus of Musselburgh

'Mad Mick of Musselburgh'. Aviator and Pig Farmer (1760 - 1792)

RARA AVIS

Known latterly as 'Mad Mick of Musselburgh', Hamish MacIcarus, 1st and last Baron Musselburgh was born at St. Andrews, Fife, in 1760 and attended the University there. The third son of a 'stickit minister', he was originally destined for Holy Orders, but it is evident that from an early age he cultivated an interest in physical elevation as opposed to that of a more spiritual nature. Whilst still a bejant at the University he became an avid disciple of the ballooning experiments of Signor Lunardi, and in his second year was rusticated for the whole of Candlemas Term for preaching an impromptu sermon on the Circumcision whilst suspended in the basket of a hot-air balloon tethered 100 feet above the Rector's garden. Whether this punishment was incurred by reason of his unorthodox choice of pulpit or through errors of doctrine is not recorded.

His claim to have invented the first autogyro — adapted from the working parts of James Watt's steam engine — has never been accepted by the Royal

Aeronautical Society. The only other witness to the unhappy affair of its inaugural test flight was one William Spurtle, a college servant, who, on the strength of a guinea bribe had become the unwitting test pilot. Having been extricated from the wreckage of the prototype and rescued from the roof of St. Salvator's Chapel, the aforesaid Spurtle was thereafter rendered totally speechless and ended his days in Bedlam. During the 1780's he made a series of successful though erratic experimental balloon flights over St. Andrews Bay, to the evident consternation of the newly-formed St. Andrews Ladies Sea-Bathing Society, before that intrepid body of women was finally abolished by order of the Kirk Authorities in 1791. He had long conceived the idea of inflating a balloon with the effluvient gas obtained as a by-product of pig-swill, and in 1792 was ennobled by his grateful albeit bemused sovereign, taking the title of Baron MacIcarus of Musselburgh, Co. Midlothian.

Unfortunately he did not survive long to enjoy this honour, perishing later in the same year as a result of lighting a favourite churchwarden pipe in his balloon whilst flying over Loch Leven. Greatly mourned by the neighbourhood, which had long relied upon him as a continued subject of amused speculation and tavern wagers, his remains are scattered over five shires.

Rebecca, Baroness Harridan
'Red Rebecca of the Glens' (1767 - 1814)

During the fifty-odd years from 1790, the Highland Clearances were a national scandal, one of the most bizarre and ultimately futile stories in the whole of this sad era is that of Rebecca, Baroness Harridan of Kinbrace, who, on account of her henna'd hair was known throughout Sutherland as 'Red Rebecca of the Glens'.

The Harridans had been settled in Kinbrace since the reign of King James V, when they had been sub-feudal tenants of the Earls of Mucklemoor. Through judicious marriage arrangements and a weather-eye ever open for the main chance, they had steadily climbed the rungs of the petit-noblesse, gaining ten thousand acres in every generation, and a Barony from the Hanoverian masters to whom they were ever ready to toady, until by the middle of the eighteenth century they had sizeable holdings in a black cattle economy.

Rebecca, an only child, had succeeded to the title in 1788, but preferring the social whirl of Edinburgh, had neglected her inheritance save for regular withdrawals of money to settle her extravagant milliner's bills. The advent of the Great Cheviot Sheep had caused her little anxiety as few were likely to appear in Charlotte Square, and she would not have recognized them in any case. The year 1792, when the Edinburgh mob took to the streets for three days and the Dundases were burnt in effigy, was also known as 'Blaidhna nan Caorach' — The Year of the Sheep. It is sad to reflect that if blood is thicker than water, money is often thicker than either, and Lady Harridan, her senses alerted to the danger of losing profits from the estates she had hitherto enjoyed without effort, was sent scurrying north to install her 'four-footed clansmen' as they were ironically dubbed. Wishing to look the part, she engaged the services of an Inverness seamstress, and, inspired by the porcelain figurines she had espied in the salons of Edinburgh, she now affected the pseudo-rustic attire of a Dresden Shepherdess, and roamed her estates, complete with a flowered straw hat and shepherd's crook.

Since the sum total of her farming knowledge had been gleaned from the pictures in her Nursery books, she experienced no small measure of difficulty in coming to terms with rural life. Her initial problem lay in distinguishing between any species other than cats, dogs, or horses. She was completely baffled when it came to questions of gender. Rams and ewes were a mystery to her town-bred mentality, and one Billy-goat, having narrowly escaped the unique experience of being milked, took to the hills and was never seen again. On a later occasion, several sheep adopted a siege mentality, holing themselves up in a pen for three days and nights rather than suffer her amateur attempts at shearing. Soon tiring of this charade, and inspired by nothing more than avarice, she now set about evicting her tenants.

Warming to her self-imposed task with a vengeance surpassed only by the infamous factor Patrick Sellar, she gathered about her a small band of female acolytes. Known as 'The Daughters of Rebecca' they terrorised the surrounding countryside for several years. Mounted on horseback they would descend on isolated cottages at dead of night, demanding the surrender of tenancies with minimal compensation. Those of her tenants who put up some token show of resistance were subjected to a barrage of gutter invective, frequently non-stop for several hours on end, whilst the more obdurate were treated to cauldrons of Hotch Potch poured down their chimneys. Extreme cases were dealt with by the simple expedient of having their thatch set alight, which was eventually to prove her undoing.

The year 1814 was known as 'Bliadhna an Losgaidh' — The Year of the Burning. In an effort to evict her last tenant she set fire to his cottage, but within the space of half an hour the wind changed, consuming cottages and woodland alike to the flames. Burning her braes, the flames engulfed Harridan House itself, the glow from the inferno lighting the Sutherland skies, and could be seen from as far away as Dunnett Head. In an effort to save herself from immolation the last of the Harridans tripped in the darkness, and perished in her own sheep dip.

Barbara Keelie
Lady Strathmurdoch (1776 - 1822)

Escaping both the grime of eighteenth century Drumchapel and the lecherous advances of her father's beerhouse customers, Barbara Keelie bade farewell to Glasgow on her eighteenth birthday and took the road to Edinburgh and freedom. Having ambitions to become an actress, she first came to the attention of the critics with a minor part in Hume's 'Douglas', before catching the experienced eye of Sir Henry Raeburn, and acceded to his request for her to model for his 'Acis and Galatea', which may still be seen in the National Gallery of Scotland.

A frequent visitor to Sir Henry's studio at that period was the nonegenarian William, 7th Earl of Strathmurdoch, sitting for a portrait commissioned by the Incorporated Society of Distillers, having contributed to their profits so assiduously since his youth. Ever one to appreciate a pretty turn of ankle, and determined to disinherit his only son, Cuthbert, Master of Strathmurdoch, who had disgraced the family by joining the Temperance Movement, the aged peer pressed his suit by means of an interlocutor, one Deacon Brawlie (q.v.).

Anxious not to waste his good fortune, and determined to eradicate the painful memory of his first wife, a woman of singularly forbidding aspect who had once soundly thrashed a ghillie for tying the wrong fly, the good Earl confined his matrimonial duties to the boudoir and the bottle. He had, moreover, the distinct impression that his Maker would, before long, summon him to the enjoyment of more spiritual delights than those presently afforded. In this he was proven justified, his bodily strength being in inverse ratio to his avowed enthusiasm.

The simple dignity of his funeral in the family chapel was somewhat marred by the sudden and unannounced arrival of his heir who, choosing this moment to forswear a lifetime's teetotalism, interrupted the solemn proceedings with snatches of bawdy songs, finally

tripping over the minister's cassock, he followed his father into the vault below with near-fatal results. This singular act of filial devotion did not go unremarked, and was the prelude to a subsequent Cause Celebre, for, shortly after this obsequial pantomime, the young Lady Strathmurdoch found herself with child, her late spouse having proven his virility even from beyond the grave. The child, who was christened William, later became Member of Parliament for Edinburgh North, and was Secretary to Lord Melbourne.

Meanwhile, however, armed with a not inconsiderable fortune, Barbara became a society hostess, and Strathmurdoch House became the Mecca of the capital's intellectual and artistic elite. The young Walter Scott conceived his "Ivanhoe" there, The Friends of the People were avidly discussed, and should such sparkling conversation prove too tiring, there were discreet side rooms where gentlemen could sup a dish of tea and indulge in polite intercourse with Barbara's 'Young Ladies' as she liked to call them. In this last it was particularly fortunate that her house abutted an apothecary's shop, where the excesses of Venus could be given the attention of Mercury, and with whom she had a standing arrangement.

Her habitual high-living and natural appetites, which she allowed full rein, at length played havoc with her once-youthful looks, and she latterly became less particular in her choice of clientele. She died in 1822, on the eve of George IV's celebrated visit to Edinburgh, and is buried in Greyfriars Kirk. A rumour put about shortly after her death that her unexpurgated memoirs were to be published, brought about the speedy resignation of the Lord Provost, together with those of several livings.

43

Gracie Gingham
'The Border Lay' (1780 - 1835)

Gracie Gingham was born in 1780 in the small village of Tinto, near Coldstream in the eastern borderland, where her widowed mother was proprietress of the local tea rooms. A comely and well-proportioned girl of an obliging disposition, she was perhaps more generous than prudent in the granting of her pubescent favours, and ere long gained the questionable 'tho well-deserved soubriquet of 'The Border Lay' throughout Roxburgh and Peebles. Many were the village lads she first set on the fumbling road to manhood, and at hairst her excited giggles were a regular punctuation of the daily toil.

In the summer of her sixteenth year she fell prey to the sleekit charms of a Captain in Lord Rannoch's Fencibles, who were exercising in the locality. Shortly after the return of the regiment to its garrison at Berwick-on-Tweed, it became increasingly apparent that the gallant young Captain's tactics in the field would bear fruit by the following Spring. Her erstwhile paramour, observing the mores of the military of the time, had omitted to provide her with a forwarding address, considering the leaving of his cap badge sufficient token of his undying esteem; upon hearing from a brother officer of her enquiries concerning his whereabouts, he hastily removed his young wife and children from their tenement lodgings and applied for service overseas with the East India Company, leaving Mistress Gingham to fend for herself.

Her plight would indeed have become desperate had it not been for her serving an afternoon dish of tea to one, Nathaniel Vest, Curate of Chillingham, Northumberland, who was visiting the area in search of specimens for his forthcoming volume on the fauna of the Merse. Happy to relate that the said cleric's idea of field expeditions was more honourable than that of his predecessor in her affections, and, seeing the opportunity to garner a harvest for The Lord, as well as provide himself with an inexpensive housekeeper, a match was sealed within the space of a month, and by Michaelmas their troths were given and plighted. Far from relegation to a clerical backwater, Grace now found ample opportunity to exercise her generous nature in the corporal works of mercy, bringing relief to many: her spouse had the worldly charity to turn an indulgent, if not blind eye to her occasional nocturnal forays and subsequent absences from the breakfast table.

Her son, The Rt. Reverend Cedric Gingham-Vest D.D., was appointed Auxiliary Bishop of Papua-New Guinea in 1846, but was unfortunately eaten by his parishioners two years later, after an altercation over the Diocesan Annual Accounts. Grace died, a satisfied woman, in 1835, pre-deceasing her husband by some six months, and a monument in the south transept of Chillingham Parish Church pays tribute to her charitable

works to the deserving poor, as well as to the excellence of her vicarage teas. Her most lasting memorial, however, is the famous Gingham tartan, whose distinctive red and white chequers have graced many a young girl, and not a few picnic spreads. Hunting setts in both blue and green are woven, but these have not to date been approved by Lord Lyon.

Edward Boke
'Typhoid Ted the Turnpike Terror' (1785 - 1819)

Today's motorway driver, having survived the homicidal boorishness of multi-wheeled juggernauts, and the lemming-like vagaries of coast-bound traffic, pulls in to a Service Area in search of refreshment. Encountering perhaps three or four hundred of like intent, and passing the serried ranks of fruit machines, he is processed through the conveyor belt of hamburgers, soggy vegetables, limp salads, and a hundred million chips. Paying heavily for the privilege of being treated with the indifferent arrogance of those enjoying a monopoly franchise, he clutches his plastic 'cutlery' as he squeezes his way to a sticky table and the questionable eating habits of his close neighbours. All this he suffers to the continuous din of piped music and the all-pervading odour of plebian greasiness.

Small wonder, then, that in a more reflective moment he might hearken back to a more gracious age of travel — the era of the stage coach. In his mind's eye he sees gabled roofs and cobbled yards where friendly ostlers, full of rustic wisdom, tend the steaming horses. Rubicund landlords heartily pour pewter tankards of good March beer, with ever a merry quip and jest on their lips as they gratefully accept two shillings for a night's lodging and Dinner in the Bar Parlour. Forelocks are touched with due subservience, and cheeky, whistling tapsters serve as travellers' tales are told beside the dying embers of the fire. He may dream of a buxom serving wench with dark, floating curls, whose flickering candle lights the way to a low-beamed room, where lavender-scented sheets are turned down as the brass warming pan is removed. "… and should the Young Master require anything else…" — and with a curtsey she takes her leave. All this he may dream, such is the wishful thinking of the popular imagination, fostered by the late Mr. Dickens and the mass-manufacturers of Christmas cards.

Edward Boke, second son of the local knackersman, was born in the pleasant border village of Langholm in 1785. Apprenticed to the newly-established cotton mill at thirteen years, he soon tired of the life, and breaking his indentures, determined to try his luck as a highwayman and live by his wits. As his wits were somewhat less than sharp, and his steed but recently reprieved from his father's premises, his career was less than spectacular, and came to an ignominious end when his mount was shot from under him by an irate passenger who disagreed with his proposals for the redistribution of her wealth. Mournfully contemplating the wreck of so promising a future, he realised with sudden insight that he had been (or at least until recently) sitting on a fortune, and Ragout de Cheval was born.

Investing his meagre and ill-gotten gains in the rent of a

derelict but-and-ben, and purchasing the services of a whey-faced slattern by the name of Ella Fankle — commonly known as Salmon Ella, who had recently been dismissed from her employment at a local hostelry by reason of her insanitary habits and culinary short-cuts, he exchanged one type of highway robbery for another, and opened a wayside cookshop. By the enterprising 'tho drastic measure of digging a series of potholes in the road adjacent to his premises, he was able to gain a fair amount of passing trade, and it was his proud boast that there was not beast, fowl, nor fish, which with the judicious addition of suitable local herbs, could not be consumed by humankind. Small animals, caught under the wheels of a passing post chaise, were apt to find themselves added to the Plat du Jour, and immortalised under the guise of Potage Herrisson or Langues de Chat en Croute, for it was to his mind axiomatic that nothing put into his ambit by a benevolent Providence should be lightly cast aside nor wasted. The contents of his Haggis were a catalogue of zoological incongruity, whilst the ingredients of his 'Cullen Skink' — a dish every bit as disgusting as its name implies — were best left unspoken. Few were the days when his customers were not presented with such epicurean delights as Souris au Gratin, or his celebrated Chien à la Royale, which filled the local hospital within six hours, and the advent of his Hamster Vindaloo is still spoken of in those parts. An Admiralty contract for his special Black Bun to be used as ballast in His Majesty's ships did much to bring his name to a wider public, but he met his end in 1819 as a result of sampling a dish of his own Cock a Leekie. He is buried in the local churchyard but it is significant that local bird and animal life gives his grave a very wide berth.

Sir Ranald MacAroni of MacAroni
'The Brummel of the North' (1791 - 1857)

Sir Ranald Alasdair MacAroni of MacAroni turned his vapid gaze from McHeep, his valet and looked out of the dressing room window. Yes — there they were still, — the three fir trees standing clear against the Midlothian sky — a perpetual reminder of his Jacobite dreams. He sighed with satisfaction and turned again to the business in hand. Dressing for a meal was always a problem, the choice in his wardrobe was so wide. He finished buttoning his woollen vest and pulled the fine linen shirt over his mane of silver hair — not so much now as there used to be, the hairline had receded a little further again this month, time to send to Edinburgh for another bottle of the Lavender-scented Hair Elixir, as blended by Appointment to his late Majesty King George IV... ah yes — those were the days...

He pulled himself from his reverie with a start, and, taking the kilt from McHeep, began to wrap it around his considerable girth. All sixteen yards of it. The dark tartan material felt good in his hands, and he loved to see the

sombre green and blue, and the dancing, gay yellow stripes of its sett. What tartan was he wearing today? — he could never remember — there were so many of them, Gordon, perhaps, or was it Campbell of Breadalbane? — he must remember to ask McHeep. Patiently waiting whilst the Flanders lace jabot was fastened around his pudgy neck he considered the problem of hose, and eventually decided upon a pair in MacLeod of Lewis, with castellated tops, which should go well with the new scarlet garters which had arrived by the carrier's man only that morning. He had for a moment considered wearing a different tartan on either leg, but dismissed the idea. One could go too far, he thought. He compromised by choosing a silver kilt pin with amethyst. The problem of shoes he left to his valet, it was some time since he had seen his feet in the flesh, so to speak, but he imagined it would be the black calfskins with the ghillie thongs as usual. The sporran next. He was particularly fond of sporrans — they made a man feel good! He waved away the selection placed in front of him and pointed to his own favourite, a natty number in white sealskin with six silver mounted tassels, and chain to match. The belt next, with its handsome buckle engraved with his coat of arms 'Argent, a peacock in its pride, proper'. So appropriate, he thought. The Lord Lyon, however, still refused to grant him the supporters he wanted, and with a sinking feeling he suspected he was going to lose this particular battle. He cheered himself up with thoughts of a waistcoat, and was torn between one in Dress Menzies, and another in MacMillan with horn buttons. The horn buttons won — he liked a slight rustic touch now and then. He surveyed the trees once more whilst McHeep brushed his full-cut jacket in Buchanan tartan, with the silver buttons and the Prince Charlie cuffs. . . ah! Charlie — will ye no come back again?' he mused. Now for the supreme moment, which for him was almost holy, as the plaid was fastened around his shoulders, and pinned with the great silver and cairngorm brooch — that same brooch which had been given him by no less a personage than His late Majesty himself, on the evening of his triumphal visit to Edinburgh back in 1822. He had worn a Royal Stuart plaid from that very day, as he did now. In his mind he could still hear the skirl of the pipes and the roar of the exultant crowd, with the great Sir Walter Scott himself leading the procession. Still — no time to let his mind wander now — dressing was an important business, and he had been at it for over two hours already. In a moment the dirk in its scabbard was fixed to his right hip, and the skean dubh in his stocking. Now for the claymore with its heavy basket grip, as the broad leather belt settled over his right shoulder. The word Claymore caused his face to flush a little, and a muscle in his cheek twitched in annoyance. It was disappointing to lose the chance of posing for that coffee advertisement, he thought, and even more galling to lose to that drunken buffoon of a soldier Sir Duncan Claymore. Really, the correspondence ensuing from his complaint to The Scotsman, had been most disagreeable. Never mind, Claymore had been obliged to scramble for his knighthood by a sordid deal in Vodka, like some common tradesman, whilst he, MacAroni, had received the accolade from a grateful sovereign. He blushed again at the remembrance of his Royal patron's Hanoverian ancestry. Perhaps the fir trees would have to be cut down one day. . .

Almost ready now. He waited a trifle impatiently whilst the powdered wig with its black silk bow was shaped comfortably to his head — no point in half measures — followed by his handsome glengarry, with its red and white diced headband, and the heavy silver clan brooch and three tall eagle's feathers, almost touching the chandelier. Slipping a snuff mull into his sporran, he took the heavy targe offered by McHeep, and, gripping his ancient musket by the barrel, surveyed himself in the cheval glass. 'Not bad' he thought. . . 'not too bad at all for a man of my age. . .' Not for nothing had he been dubbed The Apogee of Highland Romanticism, and he had a reputation to maintain. . . not bad at all. . . but now for some Breakfast!!

Sir Duncan Claymore
Soldier of Fortune (1815 - 1873)

It was an unfeeling Providence that ordained that Duncan Claymore should have been born in the Summer of 1815, on the day after the Battle of Waterloo, when the British nation, having survived the Napoleonic Wars of the past several years, put away the toys of conflict for a generation. His father, the celebrated amateur botanist James Claymore, had little time for his children — indeed he had no firm idea of how many he had sired, for which information he relied upon his wife — a long-suffering woman who, stultified by years of neglect, eventually sought the more reliable comforts of the gin bottle. By far the youngest of the Claymore brood, the young Master Duncan was left very much to his own devices during childhood. The gift of a box of lead soldiers from an indulgent uncle in the cavalry, encouraged his interest in military matters from an early age, and before long the nursery of the family house near Haddington resembled nothing so much as a battlefield. A succession of nannies left the house in tears after being treated either as

adversaries or unwilling hostages in his war games, and indeed one girl disappeared without so much as packing her belongings, after she had been discovered, after five days, locked in an outhouse where her young charge had incarcerated her as Napoleon on St. Helena.

Upon leaving school where he remembered only what interested him, he sought employment of a military nature, and briefly considered South America, where various emergent nations were seeking their independence. At this time Argentina was unshackling her bonds with Mother Spain, but, having wisely decided that Spain would be well rid of her after all, young Claymore looked nearer home, and, prevailing upon the good offices of the same benefactor who had given him his toy soldiers, requested him to use his influence in the purchase of a commission in Lord Rannoch's Fencibles, then serving with the British Army in India.

Apart from occasional skirmishes with Pathan tribesmen on the North-West Frontier, his military duties were undemanding, and his attention to the minutiae of military ceremonial was second to none. He did, however, incur the displeasure of his commanding officer on one celebrated occasion when he went on a three-day drinking session with the Regimental mascot — an Angora goat, after which only the latter was fit for parade. His capacity for drink on Mess nights was legendary, and generally ended-up in the shadier areas of the native quarter, over which, perhaps the veil of discretion should be drawn. His consumption of curried lamb was no less prodigious, and gained for him the unending respect of his Indian servants. Always a strong horseman, he enjoyed to the full the delights of regimental polo, and occasional tiger shoots with the Maharajah of Ranchipur, with whom he enjoyed great rapport. When these military duties proved too taxing, he escaped to the peace of the various hill stations, where the wives of fellow officers could be relied upon to provide solace. During the Crimean Campaign in 1854, he briefly returned to Europe, and was instrumental in successfully negotiating the exchange of 3000 bottles of Stolichnaya Vodka for the release of a Corporal of Horse, one William Skilwoge, who had given information to the enemy. This diplomatic interlude ended in 1857, and a grateful Lord Palmerston arranged that it was as Sir Duncan Claymore that he returned to the bosom of his regiment later the same year. The Indian Mutiny was in full ferment upon his return, and it is a tribute both to his command of languages and the loyalty he inspired among the native soldiery, that throughout the troubles the regiment, which he now commanded, remained loyal to the Crown. His claim to have invented the ubiquitous tea bag whilst on manoeuvres is often disputed, but he was flattered to be asked to pose for the label of a popular brand of coffee essence. This singular honour had been coveted by the celebrated bon viveur Sir Ranald MacAroni of MacAroni, and was the cause of much acrimonious correspondence in the pages of The Scotsman.

Sir Duncan was killed and eaten by a marauding tiger he was stalking in 1873, and his good friend the Maharajah of Ranchipur made it a point of honour to shoot the beast the following day, whereupon it was stuffed and presented to Her late Majesty Queen Victoria. Adorning the wall in one of the lesser staterooms, Sir Duncan Claymore can truly be said to reside at the home of his Sovereign.

Elijah MacHinery
Ship's Engineer (1835 - 1883)

The excellence of Scottish engineers has earned for them a well-deserved place in history, — not least in the traditions of the Mercantile Marine. Born in Greenock in 1835, Elijah MacHinery perhaps epitomises the combination of technical expertise and moral rectitude which were the hallmarks of this particular breed of men. Hailing from the home town of the illustrious James Watt, it was hardly surprising that he early in life displayed an interest in things mechanical, and it is recorded that at the age of seven years he successfully built a working steam winch, with the motive power provided by his mother's copper boiler. That the contraption exploded, causing extensive damage to the family wash-house, can be attributed more to his over-zealous fuelling than to any technical fault in its design.

Having served a seven year appenticeship in Greenock Dockyard — during which time he was in the habit of leading his fellow-apprentices in impromptu prayer meetings during tea breaks, he proceeded to sea in 1858, serving with the Cathay India Steam Navigation Co. Ltd., and within the space of ten years had risen to the rank of Chief Engineer. Over his engine room he exercised the stern though benevolent paternalism of a latter-day prophet, being wholly convinced that the orderly and regular administration of his kingdom of steel and steam was but a further apprenticeship to that greater Engine Room on High, whose boilers would never run dry, and whose pistons moved throughout Eternity. In accordance with his avowed principles, strong drink was anathema to him, and new members of his Engine Room staff would, on first reporting for duty, be the surprised and chastened recipients of a stern lecture on the dangers of irregular habits and moral turpitude. Before proceeding ashore in foreign parts, his Trimmers and Firemen would be admonished on the pitfalls awaiting them, and the snares of the Devil lurking in every doorway, and woe to those who did not heed his words! On duty every Watch would be preceded with a reading from the Good Book, and there was an appropriate text for every contingency. There was to his devout ears an earnest prayer in every bearing, and a veritable anthem in every revolution of the screw.

Due to an unfortunate accident whilst coaling ship in Bombay, he had suffered the loss of his right eye, which he had replaced on his return to that port at minimal cost. His glass eye had been purchased from an Indian taxidermist who had intended it for a Bengal tiger he was stuffing as a gift from the Maharajah of Ranchipur to H.M. Queen Victoria, and it is therefore hardly surprising that the effect was somewhat disconcerting, and lent his countenance a gaze under which the strongest hearts would flinch. On leaving watch it was his habit to remove the eye and leave it on the Engine Room coaming, thus convincing his Lascar stokers that his eye was upon them at all times, and ensuring their strict attention to duty. His presence was an inspiration at shipboard sunday services, and those of his shipmates who were so unfortunate as to die at sea, could be assured of a lengthy and fulsome panegyric extolling the virtues and merits of the deceased, as the canvas coffin was slipped over the side,

and the requisite number of fire-irons would be carefully deducted from the stores inventory.

Such was the awe in which he was held by successive Masters, that few would dare to use the telegraph or speaking tubes provided for communication between Bridge and Engine Room, and would instead send an Apprentice or Third Mate with a written note to the effect that ". . .Captain Mobey presents his compliments and respectfully requests Mr. MacHinery to go Full Astern" — or whatever message was appropriate in the circumstances. It is sad that this civilised mode of comm-unication was the very cause of his, and their, demise.

On the night of 27th/28th August 1883 the S.S. 'Cathay Trader' was in the Java Sea, twelve hours out from Batavia and proceeding in ballast to Singapore, when a gigantic tidal wave was sighted to port. The Master's orders for increased revolutions as he turned his bows to meet this imminent danger, were delayed by his inhibitions about using the voice pipe or telegraph, and, taking the seas beam-on, she capsized and sank with all hands. The eruption of Krakatoa had claimed the first of its many victims.

Bogle of that Ilk
(11th century et seq)

The surname 'Bogle' probably derives from the French 'Beau Gaillard', or 'beautiful singer', possibly a minstrel or troubador.

Cyrano de Beau Gaillard was Master of the music to Duke William in 1064, but unfortunately, owing to mal de mer, did not accompany his master on his conquest of these shores.

Guillam de Beau Gelle was Chaplain to Queen Margaret in 1090, but was dismissed his post for relapsing into Celtic practices, including the keeping of a wife and two mistresses.

In 1296 *Hugh Beaugel,* a fletcher, was attached to the gate at Forfar for stealing a brace of swans, and three days later was fined 5 merks for stealing the gate.

In 1328, *Duncan Bogulle* was Rouge Boar Pursuivant at the Treaty of Northampton. Later appointed Cromarty Herald.

At Edinburgh in 1509 *Thomas Boogull,* chargehand to Walter Chapman and Andrew Myllar, instigated

Scotland's first printing strike by demanding double pay and three assistants for using the new moveable wooden printing type. His ears were cut off after arbitration.

At Elvansfoot, Lanarkshire in 1662, one *Sterling Bangle*, a strolling player, was sentenced to be whipped at the cart's tail for committing an act of cruelty to a ferret.

At Peterhead in 1709, *Archibald Biggle*, Parish Clerk, being deep in strong drink, broke both legs whilst attempting to fly from the steeple of the parish church. In 1712 the selfsame Biggle was arraigned before the magistrates, accused of frightening God-fearing people by dressing-up as a sheep and demanding beer at a local tavern. He was fined five shillings, sentenced to be shorn, and consigned to Bedlam thereafter.

In 1796 *Duncan Bogle of that Ilk*, a Captain in Lord Rannoch's Fencibles, resigned his Commission at Berwick-on-Tweed, and applied for service with the Honorable East India Company. It was rumoured that he had seduced one Grace Gingham of Tinto, and got her

with child. He perished at Madras in 1811, of a surfeit of curried beef and cold ale.

At Edinburgh in 1802, *Josiah Beagle* registered his patent for the first steam bicycle, perishing later the same year whilst testing the contraption on the Calton Hill. The remains of his infernal machine are preserved in the Transport Museum, Leith Walk.

At Crail in 1835, *Thomas Bagle*, felt hat maker, won a wager of fifteen shillings by standing on one leg outside the Tolbooth for five days, two hours and fourteen minutes. The record was broken by an escaped stork from Glasgow Zoo in 1967.

In 1892, *Janet and Japhet Boggle,* a newly-wed couple were each fined in the sum of five shillings and made to sit in the Stool of Repentance for the space of six hours for smiling and whistling on the Sabbath.

'Rocking Rod' Bogle, born 1940, one-time bricklayer's mate, is founder and lead guitarist of the Doomtown Brats. Record-breaking tour of nine American cities 1964. Golden Discs 1964/5/6. M.B.E. for services to export 1967. Fined £1000 for possession of cannabis 1968. Tax exile 1968-71. Married (i) 1959. Jessie Sproggit of Drumchapel, 3 sons, 2 daughters. Married (ii) 1978. The Hon. Fiona Wellington-Boote, daughter of the Earl of Mucklemoor, 1 daughter. Presenter of ITV's "Bogle's Bumper Bandbox". 'Born-again' Christian 1980. Interviewed by Norman St. John-Stevas on BBC.2.

Dr Hamish MacTanistry
Genealogist and Herald, Author of the MacTanistry Papers
(1842 - 1910)

Hamish Ranald Norval MacTanistry, younger son of Dr. Lachlan MacTanistry, Minister of Drumbuckie, Fife, was born in 1842. As a son of the Manse, he was fortunate in having both a stable upbringing at home, and the use of an extensive library from an early age, the contents of which latter he availed himself to the full. His lifelong interest in the study of heraldry commenced as a schoolboy, when he correctly itemised two mistakes in the quarterings of Lord Rannoch, as depicted on a funeral hatchment in his father's church. This observation was later verified by the then Lord Lyon King of Arms, and the offending memorial was duly rectified. This early success in his chosen profession was sufficient to encourage his studies, and at the age of fifteen he catalogued all church hatchments in the Kingdom of Fife, proceeding from church to church on horseback, and faithfully recording his results in a penny notebook, purchased expressly for the purpose. This minor opus was later published, and the original notebook is lodged at the Scottish Record Office.

At the age of seventeen he went up to the University of St. Andrews, reading Law and Scottish History, and came down with a good second class degree. That he did not gain a first can probably be attributed to the amount of time he spent fishing, an interest which was to last for the whole of his life. Whilst at the University he also successfully raised sufficient funds for the restoration of the roof of St. Salvator's Chapel, which had been damaged the century before, due to the aeronautical experiments of the late Lord MacIcarus. (q.v.) Upon coming down from St. Andrews he entered the Edinburgh law firm of Messrs. Muckit and Peever, with premises in Ainslie Place, where he specialised in Peerage cases. It is recorded that he was once challenged to a duel with horse pistols by the 2nd Lord Braxie, when the legitimacy of one of that impetuous peer's ancestors was brought into question, but happy to relate that the noble lord had the grace to apologise and withdraw his

challenge when the point was verified.

In 1872 he married Lettice, younger daughter of the 5th Earl Lammastide, but, to their disappointment their union was not blessed with issue. In 1877 he severely criticised the Lord Provost of Edinburgh for the paucity of funds made available to celebrate the proclamation of Her late Majesty Queen Victoria as Empress of India, and a lengthy and at times acrimonious correspondence ensued in the pages of The Scotsman. In 1895 he was appointed Caithness Herald Extraordinary, which appointment always gave him more pleasure than any other. Never conscious of sartorial niceties, he was prone to putting on his tabard back to front, and Lord Lyon always made him the subject of a discreet yet searching inspection before public ceremonials.

Although without children of his own, he was an encourager and benefactor of the young, and led a lengthy and successful archaeological expedition of undergraduates from his Alma Mater to the Western Isles in the Summer of 1900. During this expedition a complete survey was made of the giant Iron Age football stadium at Callanish in the Outer Hebrides, and the results faithfully recorded. This was later published as a paper entitled 'The Forgotten League'.

In 1907 he demitted the office of Caithness Herald, and retired to his home at Drumbuckie, where he completed his work on the MacTanistry Papers. He continued to fish for Salmon, generally on Loch Aidle, where he once caught a 29 lb fish with a dry fly dressed from two or three loose threads from his kilt. He died in 1910, his wife Lettice having pre-deceased him by only three weeks, and is buried in the family vault at Drumbuckie.

His most lasting memorial, however, is the MacTanistry Scholarship in Heraldic Studies, awarded annually at the University of St. Andrews, and last year awarded to a young student from Nigeria for his paper on family symbolism on Yoruba shields.

Couthyson of Lumreekie
'Oor Wee Andy'. Music Hall entertainer (1892 - 1973?)

Andrew Couthyson or 'Oor Wee Andy' as he was latterly known was born at Lumreekie, Lanarkshire, in 1892, the youngest child in a family of fourteen Celtic supporters. His father, always fond of travelling, walked out the day after he was born, leaving his mother to keep the family on her meagre earnings as cleaner to one of Glasgow's lesser-known music halls. Too young to be left at home, the young Andrew was obliged to accompany his mother to her place of work, and it was probably his early introduction to the company of actors (never advisable at such a tender age) that helped to sow the seeds of his subsequent career and inevitable downfall.

Upon leaving school — where his piping treble rendition of 'Lochaber No More' had brought tears to many an eye — and many an itching boot, he eschewed the honest employment his mother had obtained for him with the Sewerage Department of Lanarkshire County Council, and departed south to seek his fortune on the London stage.

After some time playing 'bit parts' in repertory he fell in with a cynical agent who should have known better, and therefore shares some measure of culpability in the matter. Together they contrived an 'act' which for bogus rusticity, near-blue humour, second-rate music, and whisky-breathing sentimentality, has few equals in the annals of the stage. Spurning the Gaelic poets and Ceol Mor of a more glorious age, this debased cultural coinage was passed-off as the genuine article to a credulous public which knew no better. Swathed in whatever tartan caught the Wardrobe Mistresses' eye, horsehair sporran down to the knees, and brandishing a cromach that had been no further north than the Edgeware Road, he finally convinced a whole generation of the English theatre-going public that Scotland was a cultural backwater. He loved a 'Bonnie Wee Lassie', the heather was always 'purrple', Aberdonians were misers, Glaswegians drunkards, and having thus slandered his fellow-countrymen he would assure his audience that his heart

was in the 'Hielands'. In the highlands of Sauchiehall Street it might well have been, but his agent was safely in Shaftesbury Avenue, and the money rolled in.

A discreet curtain should be drawn over his wartime efforts on behalf of ENSA, suffice to say that the Reich considered awarding him the Knight's Cross (with Oak Leaves) for damage to British morale, and after a particularly disastrous concert party in Cairo in 1942, a company of The Black Watch, trying to enjoy a well-earned leave, were so incensed by this tartan-clad apparition that they summarily dealt with him in a manner the mention of which forever brought a blush to his already rubicund countenance.

After the war his fortunes declined, apart from occasional appearances on 'Workers' Playtime', and the annual television 'spot' on New Year's Eve. He was once short-listed as Rector of Glasgow University, but was beaten to the post by a prominent Trade Unionist. For some years he made appearances singing at Burns Suppers on the southern Caledonian Society circuit, and he was last seen in the early seventies, cleaning glasses in a public house near St. Martin's Lane.

Sir Mungo MacHismo Bt
Entrepreneur (1942 -   )

Sir Mungo MacHismo, 17th Baronet of Nova Scotia, is part of the great British entrepreneurial tradition which inspired such success stories as the Darien Expedition, the South Seas Company, and the Groundnut Scheme. Born in an Anderson shelter in 1942 at the height of an air raid by one of our Common Market partners, he perhaps had good enough reason to consider that life was against him from the start. His business career commenced at the age of nine when he employed a number of his schoolfriends on a piece-work basis in the manufacture of toy soldiers, fashioned from lead which he had previously stripped off the roof of the local parish church. It also says much for his sense of fair play that no less than 5% of his takings found itself in the collection plate on the following Sunday. Part of the proceeds of this venture were invested in the rudimentary furnishing of one wing of the family home during the following Summer holidays, where he covertly housed a group of ten families from County Kerry for a period of six weeks.

His erstwhile tenants, who were willing to pay cash in advance and no questions asked, saw nothing strange in being obliged to enter and leave their temporary accommodation on tiptoe during the few hours of Summer darkness, and would have gone completely undetected had it not been for one of their number, awash with several pints of Guinness and noisily lachrymose over the death of his favourite auntie in Dublin, having been picked up by the local constabulary and obliged to give his current address.

A brief period of military service in The Rannoch Highlanders (formerly Lord Rannoch's Fencibles) was brought to an ignominious end when questions were asked about the regular disappearance of military vehicles whilst on night exercises with BAOR, and which found themselves on the other side of the East German border bearing new markings and a fresh coat of paint, and he deemed it prudent to resign his commission.

In 1967 his father, the turf-loving 16th Baronet, having

dissipated what remained of the family fortune on a succession of fast women and slow horses, finally departed at odds of 7/2 for that great Winners Enclosure in the Sky, leaving young Mungo the proud possessor of a baronetcy, several thousand torn-up betting slips, and a well-thumbed address book. The monumental death duties by which governments of all political colour encourage us to be good and honest citizens, now determined the newly-fledged Sir Mungo to embark on further commercial ventures. A chance encounter with an impressionable gentleman from Seattle who was sampling the delights of Troon and had a handy swing with a No.5 iron, enabled him to raise the necessary 'greenies' for the purchase of the paddle-steamer *Sir Ivanhoe* — recently pensioned-off from ferrying holiday-makers on Loch Ness, and the MacHismo Steam Navigation Co. Ltd. was born. The passengers he transported from the Kyle of Lochalsh to the Outer Hebrides, whilst nervously clutching the stern rail of this sea-going monstrosity, and fervently wishing they had stayed safely on terra firma, would be further dismayed to notice that in the area of 'flags-of-convenience' Sir Mungo had broken new ground by having his vessel registered in the Central African Republic, whose multi-coloured ensign he proudly flew. On the eve of the company's imminent collapse in 1972, his vessel, now re-named the s.s. *Bokassa* conveniently foundered off Renish Point, her crew and single passenger having wisely taken to the lifecraft.

Sir Mungo's American partner, anxious to recoup at least part of his losses, next unwisely agreed to participate in a scheme whereby gullible customers in the United States could receive by post 'A Genuine piece of Rannoch Moor turf, complete with sprig of Scottish Heather, and tartan-backed plaque, inscribed with YOUR NAME and CLAN.' All this for $10.50c!! Although it must be admitted that the first hundred or so of these packages to be despatched were the genuine article, Sir Mungo later found it more convenient to have supplies of his raw materials closer to hand, and sad to relate that large tracts of Wimbledon Common have disappeared in this way.

In 1978, in partnership with an old friend from army days called 'Bungo' Brize-Norton, he opened a take-away Haggis and Neep Shop in the King's Road. Called 'Mac the Knife', it was a roaring success until Bungo got drunk one night and picked a fight with a bunch of 'skinheads'. The place was wrecked in ten minutes, but the insurance had unfortunately lapsed the day before.

Sir Mungo's latest venture into the lucrative worlds of catering and entertainment, has been the founding, in partnership with his friend man-about-town Berkeley Kritten, of 'The Highland Fleece', a discotheque and night club for gullible tourists, in London's West End. In its brief existence it has avoided police prosecution by the imaginative founding of the "Countryman" bar, where over-tired detective-sergeants can forget their troubles and refresh themselves for an hour or twain without the tiresome necessity of paying for their own drinks. 'The Highland Fleece' goes from strength to strength and has recently featured the American singer Barry Menopause in cabaret.

Glossary of Scottish terms

Aidle: Foul water.

As Eugmhais Gliocais: Without Wisdom.

Baillie: Municipal Official, equivalent to Eng. Alderman.

Bejant: First Year Undergraduate of University of St. Andrews. Nickname from Fr. 'Bec Jaune'.

Bhuaildh me le bata: I was hit on the head with a stick.

Biggin: Building.

Bizzem: A bad girl; a randy woman.

Blaidhna an Losgaidh: The Year of the Burning.

Blaidhna nan Caorach: The Year of the Sheep.

Bogle: A hobgoblin, a ghost.

Boke: To vomit.

Braxie: A sheep that has died of disease.

Brae: Slope or upper part of hill.

Brawlie: Finely, very well. Daein Brawlie: Doing well.

Breeks: Breeches, trousers.

Breenge on: To carry on regardless.

But-an-ben: Small cottage, house with only two rooms.

Caora Dubh: A black sheep.

Ceol Mor: The Great Song. Traditional bagpipe music.

Cheetie: A cat.

Claymore: Traditional Scottish broadsword with basket grip.

Clootie (Auld Clootie): The Devil, Satan.

Couthy: Kind, gentle. Can also infer Over-sentimental.

Cromach: Walking stick with crook handle.

Dirk: A short sword.

Drumlie: Muddy.

Eident: Busy, diligent.

Fankle: An untidy disorder, a mess.

Fasheous: Troublesome.

Ghillie: Gamekeeper, one who accompanies at field sports.

Glengarry: Type of headgear.

Gloamin: Dusk, twilight.

Guid-willie-waucht: A good long drink.

Glaiket: Foolish.

Hairst: Harvest.

Hatchment: Armorial mourning board. Freq. found in churches.

Hotch-Potch: Thick soup or stew.

Jarl: Viking overllord. Orig. of Eng. Earl.

Kirk: Church.

Lammas: Scottish Law Term, formerly a harvest festival. Candlemas.

Lum: Chimney.

Manse: Minister's house.

Midden: Dunghill.

Muckit: Messy, dirty.

Muckle: Big, much.

Orlop: The lowest deck of a three-decked ship.

Plaid: A long piece of tartan cloth, clasped at the shoulder and hanging down the back. Formerly an integral part of the kilt.

Peevers: Children's street game.

Provost: High Municipal Official.

Pursuivant: A junior Officer of Arms.

Reek: To smoke.

Sasines: A method of investiture in lands in Scots Law.

Sett Stick: A stick marked with thread counts for the making of tartan cloth.

Skelf: A splinter.

Sleekit: Sleek, smooth.

Sporran: In Highland dress, a leather bag fastened around the waist with a strap or belt, and hanging in front over the kilt apron.

Spurtle: A kitchen stick, used for stirring. (occ. Spirtle.)

Soutar: A cobbler.

Tabard: Embroidered surcoat worn by Officer of Arms on State occasions.

Tanistry: Ancient Scottish system of appointing King by election.

Uisge Beatha: 'Water of Life', Whisky.